X

*Insect
Travelers*

By the Same Author

Birds in Flight
Chimney Swift
Fish Hawk
Winds and Weather
Wings, Sun, and Stars

John
Kaufmann

INSECT TRAVELERS

William Morrow and Company   *New York 1972*

The author wishes to thank Dr. Howard Topoff,
associated with the Department of Animal Behavior,
Museum of Natural History, New York City,
for reading the manuscript of this book.

Kaufmann, John.
  Insect travelers.

  SUMMARY: Discusses the travels of insects—how they time them,
where they get the power for them, and how they navigate.
  1. Insects—Migration—Juvenile literature. [1. Insects—Migration]
I. Title.
QL496.2.K38   595.7′05′2   72-1546
ISBN 0-688-20036-2
ISBN 0-688-30036-7 (lib. ed.)

FOR
MARGUERITA,
who always shares her joy
in natural things

Contents

*Insect
Travelers*

I
Why Insects Travel

Early one spring morning, in the northeastern United States, thousands of winged ants split open their pupal cases. The sun silvers their wings as they flutter upward from a shadowy clearing toward the brilliant light of the sky. The tiny fliers ascend higher and higher, then drift away on the wind.

On the East African plains a gray cloud swells up on the horizon. Minutes pass. The cloud looms higher and wider as it approaches. A sound like a great waterfall fills the air, and soon the sky is choked with millions of glistening, whirring wings. A great swarm of hungry desert locusts descends upon the land and strips bare every plant and tree. Before their flight stops, they will cut a swath of destruction more than a thousand miles long.

Millions of small, brightly colored, delicately patterned wings glitter in the sky over the Mediterranean Sea. An immense flock of painted lady butterflies heads out toward the flat, blue horizon, moving north from the coast of Africa. On and on they beat their paper-thin wings. After hours of flying they reach the southern coast of France. There they rest and sip nectar from blossoms. Finally, after climbing through high Alpine passes, the painted ladies end their journey in the meadows of central France and England.

Winged ants setting forth upon the wind, locusts eating their way across country, butterflies spanning the sea. These insects are just a few whose journeys place them among the greatest travelers in the natural world.

That such small and seemingly fragile creatures might have the power, endurance, and sharpness of sense necessary to travel long distances is hard to imagine. Yet we now know that even the smallest insects can fly very far. Furthermore, in comparison to their size and weight, some butterflies, moths, locusts, dragonflies, aphids, and leafhoppers rival the greatest travelers among the birds.

The travels of insects range widely. Some are short daily trips for purposes of food gathering, mating, and egg laying. Others are amazing nonstop journeys of well over a thousand miles. Then, too, there are puzzling flights in which moths move farther north as autumn approaches or butterflies head out over the widest oceans to seemingly certain death. These movements raise certain questions. Why do insects travel? What determines the time of the trip? How do they find their way?

Many species of insects travel. Such movement is a vital part of their activities during certain periods of their lives. After hatching from the egg, the young insect appears either as a nymph that will split its body casing several times as it gets larger, or as a growing,

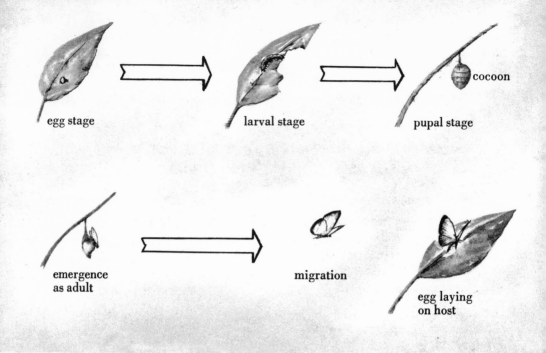

egg stage

larval stage

pupal stage

cocoon

emergence
as adult

migration

egg laying
on host

Migration is a vital part of the lives of many insects.

crawling larva that will spin a cocoon to encase itself
during its transformation into an adult. Finally, when
the last nymphal skin is shed, or the cocoon is broken
open, the adult insect emerges into the world. Blood
pumps into slender wing veins. The wings expand from
tightly crumpled shapes into thin, brightly colored or
translucently silver surfaces. Soon, after drying and
stiffening in the air, they are beating and carrying the
insect on its way.

Along with countless others of its kind the insect takes to the air and travels to find another place to live and breed. There, if it is a female, its load of eggs must be laid upon the proper kind of food, so its young can start to feed when they hatch. The monarch butterfly lays its eggs on milkweed, the beet leafhopper uses the beet plant, the black wasp finds tiny plant-sucking insects called aphids. Each species of insect searches out the particular food, or host, that will sustain its coming generation.

Certain adult insects live for one or more years and make a number of migrations. However, most insect travelers lead very short lives that last only a part of one spring or summer. Soon after they lay their eggs, these insects die. But the species goes on. Eggs hatch; young grow; adults emerge, travel, lay their eggs, and die. The cycle continues through a number of generations until the days become shorter and cooler and the chill of winter threatens. Then these cold-blooded creatures, which need warm days and nights to remain active, suspend their activities. They lapse into a state of halted growth and movement called diapause.

In various stages of life insects wait for winter to

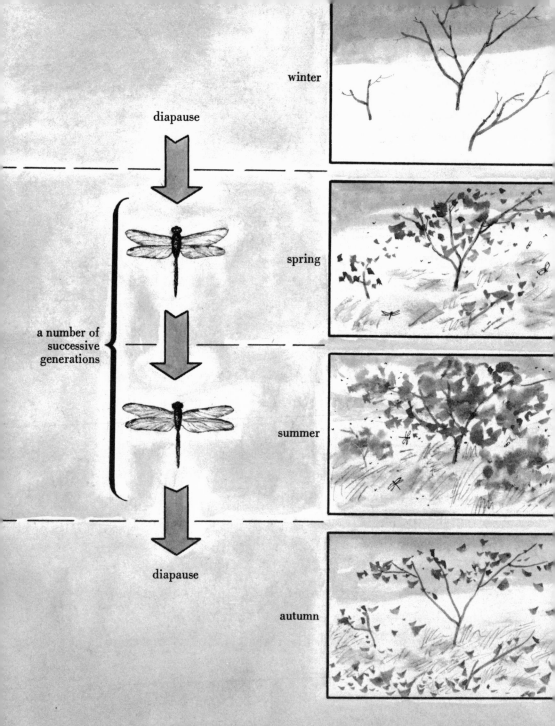

winter

diapause

a number of
successive
generations

spring

summer

diapause

autumn

insects and the seasons

pass. Beetle larvae rest under soil, rocks, and leaves. Dragonfly nymphs lie buried beneath muddy ponds. Numb butterflies cling inside shells of hollow trees. Moths nestle tightly wrapped and protected within their cocoons. Their body activity is at almost a complete standstill, so they burn very little energy and can survive for a long time. Finally, when the warm days return, insects come out of diapause and resume their interrupted lives where they left off months before. Eggs hatch, nymphs and larvae crawl, pupae develop, adults emerge and start to travel.

Young adult insects may move out into areas immediately around their breeding habitats. For example, some generations of the great southern white butterfly in Florida spread out slowly in different directions for as much as several miles. Their random movements are merely the result of their normal feeding, mating, and egg-laying activities. Such gradual flights are called dispersals. In contrast, other generations of this butterfly migrate, and they travel very differently. Large flocks head in one direction and move hundreds of miles from their original breeding area. This kind of prolonged, straightened movement is typical of all in-

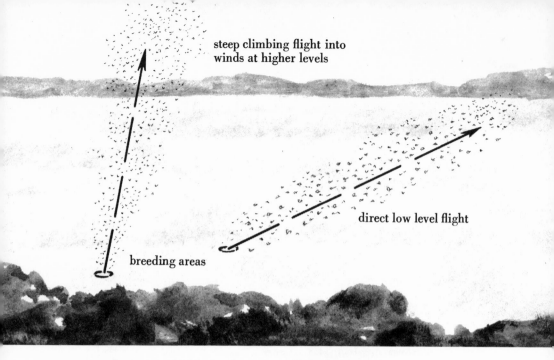

steep climbing flight into
winds at higher levels

direct low level flight

breeding areas

the two main kinds of migrant flight movements

sect migrations. White butterflies, however, are stronger
fliers than some insects and can hold a steady direction
across country despite adverse winds.

Smaller migrants, such as leafhoppers, are weaker
fliers. Normally leafhoppers fly very little, making short
hops from leaf to leaf or from one plant to another.
Nevertheless, their particular kind of straightened flight
at departure shows them to be true migrants. They beat
their wings strongly and continuously, climbing almost
vertically high into the air. This lifts them into warm

air currents called thermals rising hundreds and even thousands of feet. Once aloft, they and many other small insects support themselves by constantly flapping while fast winds carry them far across country.

Within the breeding area insects rarely follow a steady, uninterrupted path in one direction during their everyday activities. For example, when butterflies are busy with feeding, mating, or laying their eggs, they flutter from flower to flower, turning this way and that way, seldom following a straight course even across one small field.

When insects migrate, however, their whole behavior changes. They are not distracted by the flowers or plants on which they normally feed. The attraction between male and female lessens, so mating diminishes or ceases. The development of eggs within the female slows down or stops. All these normal activities are temporarily suspended when the time to travel comes. Their flight, prolonged and undistracted, allows them to escape completely from their former living places. After journeying for some time, the migrants settle down in a new breeding area. For winged ants, the whole trip may last only minutes and cover a distance of a hundred yards.

For desert locusts or monarch butterflies, the journey may take weeks and stretch well over a thousand miles.

Insects time their travels to arrive in new habitats when food supplies, breeding sites, and weather conditions are favorable. Faulty timing can prove fatal. For instance, if butterflies travel too far north too early in spring, they will not find plants with nectar for food or with leaves on which to lay their eggs. Insects inherit a sense of time that moves in tempo with the seasons. This inner clock controls and coordinates all the important activities of their lives, including migration, by signaling at the proper times to the brain nerve centers. In turn, the nerve centers release into the bloodstream hormones that regulate the important body organs.

The insect's seasonal clock is set and kept running on time by the movement of the earth orbiting the sun. This yearly rhythm causes the days in the northern hemisphere to become shorter from June 21 to December 21 and longer from December 21 to June 21. Thus, the length of day, which insects measure by the numbers of hours of daylight they receive, is an accurate indicator of seasonal time in the yearly cycle. Unlike temperature, day length does not vary from one year

Longer days and higher temperatures
cause insects to emerge and migrate.

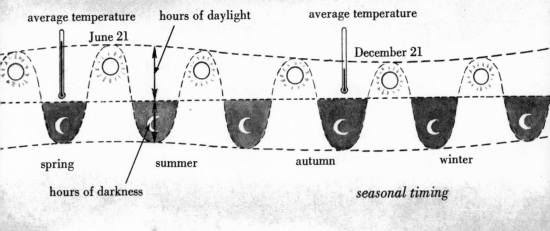

average temperature

June 21

hours of daylight

average temperature

December 21

spring

summer

autumn

winter

hours of darkness

seasonal timing

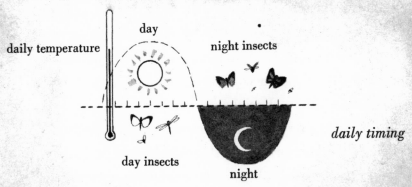

daily temperature

day

night insects

day insects

night

daily timing

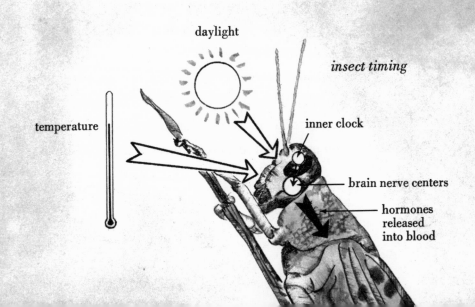

daylight

insect timing

temperature

inner clock

brain nerve centers

hormones
released
into blood

to the next, so it is a reliable, basic signal for migrations. Temperature acts as a strong secondary control and safety check on the primary timing of the inner clock by day length. Once the insect's clock signals "go," several very warm days will speed up the normal departure time. On the other hand, if a cold spell comes, the low temperature temporarily overrules the "go" signal of the inner clock.

Insects have a daily clock as well as a seasonal clock. It regulates their activities within a twenty-four hour cycle that is timed according to the alternating periods of day and night. Various insects become active at certain times of day. For example, most butterflies begin flying in the morning. Other insects, such as night-flying moths, become active toward evening. Similarly, insects depart on migration flights at certain times of day. Temperature also affects daily timing, speeding up or holding back insect activity. Thus, on a very warm day, butterflies will fly earlier, while on a cool day they fly later when the temperature is higher.

When birds, fish, and mammals migrate, the same individual creature normally journeys away from and back to the same region. When insects migrate, on the other hand, the individual usually does not make a round trip. Because their short lives do not last through even one season, most insect migrants travel only one way. Long-lived insect travelers like monarch butterflies and ladybird beetles are exceptions. These insects live through more than one season. They migrate from breeding places to distant areas where they pass the winter, then journey back the following spring.

Many migrant species cover very long distances in seasonal migrations. For example, each year in spring and early summer, the painted lady butterfly moves from northern Mexico to northeastern Canada, across thousands of miles. However, the total distance is not covered by one generation. Instead, successive generations of migrants, all moving in the same direction, combine their travels to reach the maximum range.

Although most insects spend only a short period of their lives in migration, a few have adopted travel almost as a way of life. Army ants of tropical America and driver ants of Africa stream through the jungles in winding columns numbering millions of individuals. By periodically stopping, then moving on to different areas in the same extensive breeding habitat, these fierce

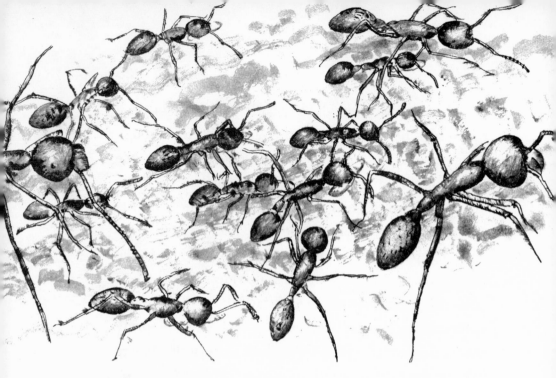

South American army ants

predators maintain a plentiful food supply. Since they are highly organized, crowding is no problem; in fact, they thrive in groups of large numbers.

The ability to travel helps many species of insects to survive. By reaching new breeding habitats, they are able to spread their numbers over wider areas and lessen population pressure. For instance, if too many black-bean aphids are crowded into one bean field, competition among them for feeding and living space on the bean plants is severe. However, if a large portion of that aphid population can migrate to other, unoccupied fields, the pressure becomes much less. By migrating, aphids find a food supply for themselves and the following generation of aphid nymphs. At the same time they have more space for living, feeding, and laying their eggs. Thus, both the aphids that migrate and those that remain behind benefit from migration. The same is true of many other species.

As insects develop and as the seasons pass, their food and other requirements change. Green plant leaves that the young, crawling caterpillars of butterflies and moths eat are of no value to the same insects when they become winged, nectar-sipping adults. By migrating, butterflies and moths reach areas where nectar-filled blossoms are plentiful. In other cases, the hosts and even the overall habitat may change during the season. For example, black-bean aphids feed and lay their eggs on bean plants, which die before the end of summer. By that time, however, their offspring already have migrated to woody shrubs and trees, which are able to survive through autumn and winter. There the aphids lay their eggs, which remain dormant until the following spring. Then new generations of black-bean aphids mature and develop before migrating to their summer plants. Thus, migration allows aphids and many other insects to reach alternate habitats that are suitable for the time of year.

In spring, crops and other plants on which insects feed mature first in southernmost regions. As temperatures gradually rise and the hours of daylight grow longer, they appear farther and farther north. By timing their migrations to match this northward advance of spring and summer, successive generations of insects are able to find the same food. The young adults of each butterfly generation feed on nectar, sometimes that from only one or a few species of plants. As a result, butterfly migrations are timed so that adults emerge where and when their particular blossoms are most plentiful. Many destructive insects also move north each year to find their favorite food. Beet leafhoppers in the southern United States feed on succulent green beet plants in late spring and early summer. During the summer, when the beet crops are cut or dry out, the leafhoppers migrate to other areas farther north where beet crops are still green.

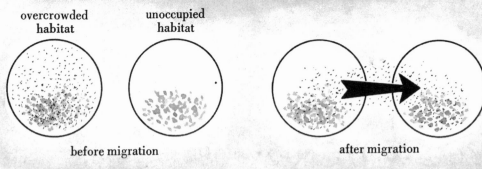

overcrowded
habitat

unoccupied
habitat

before migration

after migration

lessens population pressure

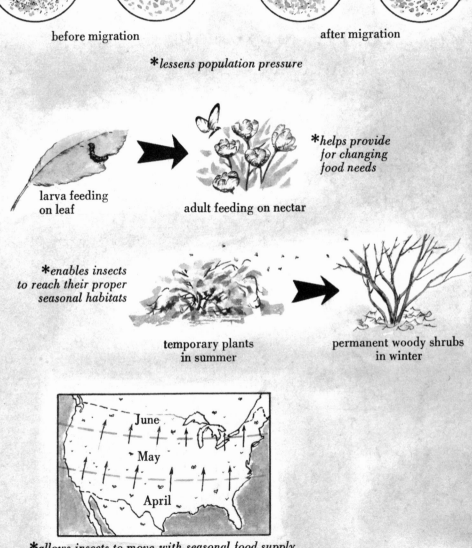

larva feeding
on leaf

adult feeding on nectar

*helps provide
for changing
food needs*

*enables insects
to reach their proper
seasonal habitats*

temporary plants
in summer

permanent woody shrubs
in winter

June

May

April

allows insects to move with seasonal food supply

*some advantages of migration**

Migration also enables insects to escape from their breeding habitat when their food disappears due to extremes in weather conditions. Many kinds of dragonflies live by small ponds that may dry up during summer drought, cutting off their food supply of flying insects that live there. By migrating, they can reach other bodies of water where their insect prey is plentiful. For this reason, a greater proportion of migrant species come from small, shallow ponds than from large bodies of water such as lakes and rivers.

Migration strengthens insect species as a whole. It enables them to widen the area where they can breed and add to their total population. Greater numbers insure the survival of a species even if cold, drought, or severe storms should kill many individuals. In addition, larger numbers increase the genetic variety of possible mating combinations, making for more adaptability.

Nevertheless, countless individual insects perish during their travels. During migration some of nature's smallest creatures are pitted against the powerful forces of wind and weather. Because insects are cold-blooded creatures, they cannot continue to beat their wings if they are overtaken in flight by cold air. They must stop

predators

drownings

insect losses during migration

flying and descend. If they happen to be over the sea, they drown. Millions of butterflies, moths, dragonflies, and other insects are found each year, washed up along seashores. The piles of motionless, wet, and ragged travelers are testimony to the disasters of migration.

Innumerable insect travelers have met their doom in the cold, descending air currents over high mountains. Eleven thousand feet up in the Beartooth Range of

Montana is a place called Grasshopper Glacier, containing many thick layers of frozen Rocky Mountain locusts. Over thousands of years locust swarms crossing the high mountains have been caught aloft and numbed in the frigid air. On landing, they quickly froze to death. The following winter, snow covered their bodies and added another layer to this strange icy record of insect mortality.

Birds also take a toll of migrating insects. Since many insects travel in large swarms or flocks, they are easy targets for a number of birds. In one instance, cabbage white butterflies migrating past Harpenden, England, were under constant attack for several days by flycatchers and sparrows. White wings covered the ground like fallen flower petals. In an area a few yards square, observers counted 425 wings, many of them creased by beak marks. Birds attacking locust swarms in the air gorge themselves until locust wings stick out from their open mouths. Swallows and swifts snap up countless small insects rising in swarms as they start to travel. Kestrels and merlins, two of the smaller falcons, prey upon migrating dragonflies, snatching them from the air with their sharp talons.

Predatory insects attack their fellow travelers. Dragonflies prey upon the rearward stragglers of butterfly flocks, as well as upon many other insects. A burrowing wasp of East Africa travels along with its prey, the desert locust. Often when a large locust swarm lands, thousands of these wasps land too. They dig burrows, drag paralyzed locusts inside, lay eggs upon them, and seal up the entrances. If the locusts fly off suddenly, the wasps quickly follow. Their attachment to the swarm is so strong that they will leave unburied locusts next to open burrows rather than be left behind.

Many insects lay great numbers of eggs to make up for their losses both in the immature stages and during travel. When vast numbers of insects migrate, the chances are that enough will survive and breed to perpetuate their species. It has been said that the possibility of a male and female termite successfully establishing a colony after their migratory flight is as likely as that of two newborn babies starting life alone on a desert island. Still, termites and many other insect travelers do succeed. Despite the hazards and losses of migration, insects make their way across both short and long stretches of the world, and so continue to thrive.

II
Travels Near and Far

On a European farm field, cockchafer beetles emerge as adults, spread their glossy, dark brown wing covers, and take off. Several hundred feet away they settle down on fruit trees and start eating the leaves. That short distance is often their entire migration. Late in summer, in southeastern Canada, monarch butter-

cockchafer beetle
(short range migrant)
small, weak flier with
limited fuel supply

monarch butterfly
(long range migrant)
large, strong flier with
plentiful fuel supply

Strong thermal lift
carries insects to
higher altitudes.

Fast, persistent winds
give longest flights.

Moderate, less persistent
winds give shorter flights.

Weaker thermal lift
carries insects to
medium altitudes.

Winds and weather affect distances of migration.

flies beat their wide orange-and-black wings as they head south. Many weeks later they reach the southern United States or northern Mexico after flapping and sailing as far as 2000 miles. One species crosses a field; another traverses a continent. Cockchafers, monarchs, and other insect migrants differ markedly in how far they travel.

Although each species does not always migrate the same distance, insects can be divided generally into short- and long-range migrants. Large insects, such as butterflies, moths, dragonflies, and locusts, have a greater ability to make long trips than do small insects like fruit flies, leafhoppers, and aphids. Often the large, strong fliers travel low and maintain a straight course independent of wind direction. Most small, weak fliers, however, move on fast winds aloft rather than under their own power close to the ground. Therefore, the wind determines to a great extent how far they will be able to go.

Actually wind is an important factor in the length of any flight, and both large and small migrants make their longest nonstop trips by taking advantage of persistent winds aloft. At times, perhaps when strong thermals help them to gain altitude rapidly, insects ride along on vast rivers of wind and cross entire continents and oceans. Under these exceptional conditions, both small and large migrants show amazing endurance as they fly far beyond their breeding range. Some irresistible impulse seems to push them on. Of course, once insects find themselves over the ocean, they must keep going. If they touch down they will perish. They push on, straining every molecule of energy from their bodies. Aphids from Europe end up on the arctic snows, moths from Africa land in England, and monarch butterflies from the United States cross the Atlantic Ocean to Europe.

Fruit flies are only about three sixteenths of an inch long, but they cause great crop losses when they appear in tremendous numbers and lay their eggs on fruit trees. Scientists release and retrap fruit flies and other small pests to study how they move over short distances from one infested area to another. They mark the insects by staining them with colored dye, by exposing them to radioactive materials, or by removing one leg. After freeing the insects, they check traps located at various distances for any recaptures. In Greece, entomologists released olive fruit flies in the mountains and tried to trap them as they moved down toward nearby plains. After twenty-four hours they did not find any fruit flies more than 800 yards away. After ten days, they did not capture any beyond 1400 yards. In other tests, oriental fruit flies did not reach traps set two miles away. Judging from these experiments, fruit flies seem to be strictly short-range travelers.

However, there are serious drawbacks to such tests. First, the number of insects recaptured is very small compared to the number released. If a few individuals out of 10,000 are caught, the results are considered better than average. Many insects undoubtedly escape by traveling upward, over, and beyond the traps, riding on thermal currents and winds.

Whenever possible, scientists try to use aerial traps in addition to ground traps. Nets are towed by aircraft, and suction traps are lifted to various altitudes by big balloons. Their motor-driven propellers suck in large amounts of air and any insects flying past. A mechanism separates the catch hour by hour, to show which insects are traveling at different times of day or night. By trapping insects aloft, scientists have found that fruit

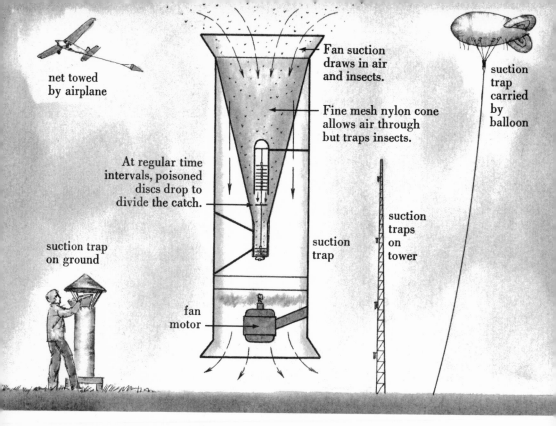

net towed
by airplane

Fan suction
draws in air
and insects.

Fine mesh nylon cone
allows air through
but traps insects.

suction
trap
carried
by
balloon

At regular time
intervals, poisoned
discs drop to
divide the catch.

suction trap
on ground

suction
trap

suction
traps
on
tower

fan
motor

trapping insects at various altitudes

flies and other small travelers sometimes climb much
higher than once was supposed. Various species of fruit
flies have been caught in aircraft nets as high as 5000
feet. Oriental fruit flies have been captured on mountains at a height of 7600 feet.

Other evidence also indicates that fruit flies are capable of traveling farther than they did in the trapping

experiments. When tested in laboratory wind tunnels, they have flown for as long as five hours, the equivalent of thirty miles, without help from the wind. In one actual case on record, fruit flies were captured on ships as far as 270 miles southeast of Japan when northwest winds blew out over the Pacific Ocean. Apparently strong winds sharply increase the distance they are able to cover.

Exceptional wind conditions stretch the range of many insect travelers. Spruce aphids, destructive pests of northern spruce forests, are about the same size as fruit flies, but they are famous for having made the longest known nonstop flight by any small migrant. On August 8, 1924, a scientist discovered thousands of spruce aphids on the arctic islands of Spitsbergen. They were still alive on the snow, spread about thirty to forty yards apart over an area several miles wide. No spruce aphids breed there, because the climate is too cold, so the insects had to have come from the south. The nearest breeding sites, however, were in the Kola Peninsula of the Soviet Union, 800 miles to the southeast across the sea.

To find out where the migration originated, the sci-

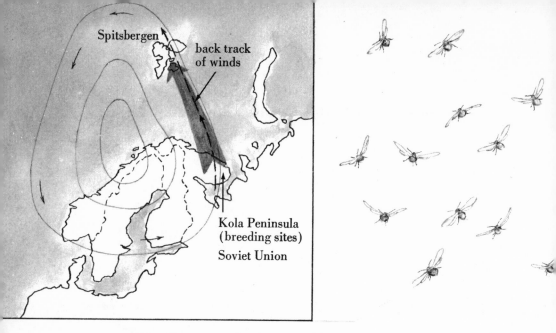

an 800-mile journey by spruce aphids

entists used a method called backtracking. They checked
the weather charts of all the areas within hundreds and
even thousands of miles of the invasion site for the
immediately preceding days. In this way they showed
that strong, steady southeast winds had been blowing
from the Kola Peninsula to Spitsbergen. Aided by
strong tail winds and fighting for their lives, the spruce
aphids must have flown for about twenty-four hours
nonstop over the icy sea. That such tiny insects could
fly so long and so far is little short of incredible.

Like spruce aphids, most beetles also are considered

insect pests. They lay their eggs on crops, ornamental plants, fruit trees, and forest trees, and their young feed on the host after hatching. However, the familiar orange-and-black ladybird beetle, or ladybug, feeds ravenously upon destructive aphids and scale insects, and so helps man to fight pests that harm his crops. As a result, the movements of ladybirds are of great interest to scientists.

Ladybird beetles sometimes appear in tremendous numbers during migration. In April, 1939, near Alexandria, Egypt, millions of eleven-spot ladybirds flew ashore from the Mediterranean Sea. Along the water's edge, they lay piled in a drift line about one foot wide, five inches deep, and fourteen miles long. One scientist estimated the number of drowned ladybirds at 4500 million. On the south coast of England, in July and August, 1952, seven-spot ladybirds lay piled in a drift line forty miles long. Similar mass sightings have been reported from France, Germany, and Spain.

Ladybird beetles are among the longest-lived adult insects, surviving for two to three years. Many species migrate to and from mountains, where they mass together under stones, leaves, or out in the open during

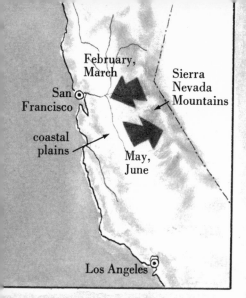

February,
March

Sierra
Nevada
Mountains

San
Francisco

coastal
plains

May,
June

Los Angeles

*migrations of convergent
ladybirds in California*

convergent ladybirds migrating

*sixteen-spot ladybirds
during diapause*

the winter. They also may travel back to the mountains in summer to escape heat and drought by lapsing into a hot-weather diapause called aestivation. Thus, some species of ladybirds may make several trips back and forth in one year.

One winter, in England, Professor C. B. Williams watched three to four thousand sixteen-spot ladybirds huddled on a gatepost of the Rothamstead Experimental Station. At first, Williams thought that the gatepost was only a temporary resting place. But the beetles stayed there, exposed to rain, snow, and freezing winds, from November until early May. During warm days in April some of the beetles became active and departed. But not until May, when the thermometer rose to seventy-two degrees, did most of the group fly away.

In California, ladybirds emerge from diapause in February and March at altitudes of about 5000 feet in the Sierra Nevada Mountains. They fly upward with a persistent movement and encounter prevailing easterly winds that blow toward the coastal plains, about a hundred miles away. There they breed. After feeding on aphids and scale insects in the fruit groves, they migrate again in May and June, when prevailing winds blow from the west toward their mountain aestivation sites.

Early in this century, entomologists in California collected millions of ladybirds from the mountains in winter. They kept the beetles in cold storage until spring, then released them in orchards and on farms to combat the aphids. However, few of the ladybirds remained in the area, and the scientists made tests to check their dispersal. They released more than 400,000 ladybirds marked with gold or silver paint in one field in the Imperial Valley. In three weeks of careful searching they found only nineteen marked ladybirds within a five-mile radius of the release point. For the next test, the scientists released 600,000 ladybirds, but after two weeks recovered only two. Obviously the beetles had departed in great numbers, even though the area was one to which they normally migrated. Evidently when the time came, they had to perform an actual migration.

Leafhoppers are about the same size as ladybird beetles, but travel longer distances. They suck plant juices and carry plant diseases. Many species, such as the beet leafhopper, are specialists, using one or two

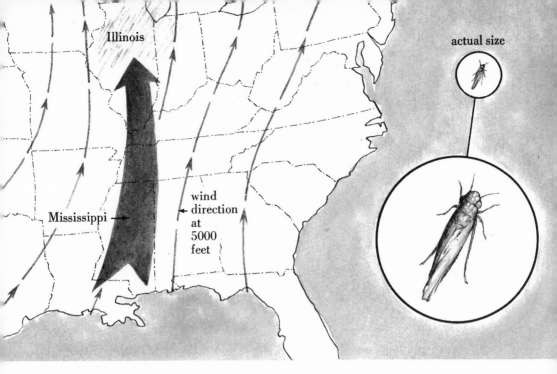

a 500-mile journey of potato leafhoppers

kinds of farm crops as their hosts. Successive generations of leafhoppers travel northward in spring as their
host crops appear in farm fields.

Potato leafhoppers are pests of potatoes, alfalfa, and
other crops in the north central and eastern United
States. Most spend the winter in the lower Mississippi
valley, but migrate north each spring. Potato leafhoppers have been caught at altitudes up to 4000 feet as
they travel hundreds of miles in one or two days on

continual warm southerly winds. Their flights, like those of many other migrants, often end when cold, sinking air and rain force them down. One invasion from May 10 to May 12, 1959, occurred in Illinois on an airstream running directly from Mississippi at an altitude of 5000 feet. At that point a heavy rainfall over most of Illinois forced the leafhoppers to land after a nonstop journey of 500 miles or more.

Certain insects, including some species of butterflies, often travel without the aid of the wind. Because they are strong flapping fliers, these insects can follow a steady course close to the ground despite unfavorable winds. Great southern white butterflies travel low, following Florida's east coast. On two-inch white wings, edged in front with a dark line, they sparkle above the sand dunes in flocks, migrating considerable distances along a narrow chain of coastal islands. In other regions farther inland, whites are known to fly higher with the wind. However, if they did so in shore regions, they would be in danger of drifting out to sea on an offshore wind. By traveling low, they can control their course and stay near the coastal islands, where their host plant, *Batis maratima,* grows abundantly.

great southern white butterflies

While making what are probably the most complete studies of any insect migrations, Erik and Astrid Nielsen of Denmark followed flights of Florida whites. They kept up with one flock by car for three hours over fifteen miles. The whites start traveling in the morning and follow the shoreline, roads, or telephone lines to maintain their course. In brisk crosswinds, they sometimes fly low in the lee of sand dunes where the air is calmer. Large flocks fly for considerably longer hours than small flocks. Some individuals travel much farther than others, up to as much as eighty miles in one day. After two days all travel ceases and the whites settle down. Finally, ten days after they first take wing as adults, the white butterflies die.

By far the most frequently observed insect migrant in North America is the monarch butterfly. Its broad, four-inch wings and its bold patterns of orange, black, and white are a conspicuous and familiar sight. The breeding grounds of this famous traveler are throughout much of the United States and southern Canada. Monarchs start to move south in late August and early September, usually in twos and threes. Sometimes they assemble in small groups, and occasionally they form massed flocks that fill the sky. However, their numbers are much less now than formerly, judging by early reports of their migration. One description tells of swarms of monarchs mounting on high like orange-tinted clouds several miles wide and long, surging forward toward the south, casting wide shadows on the sunlit plains.

When monarchs traveling south from Canada reach the north shore of the Great Lakes, they settle down

at dusk to roost near the water's edge. If the next morning is sunny, they may head out straight across the
water, although no shore is visible on the other side.
Steady streams of monarchs often move southward
along Pelee Point, a peninsula jutting down into Lake
Erie. Other monarchs take the long way around Lake
Erie and Lake Ontario.

Monarchs also fly the same coastal route that birds
follow down the Atlantic shore. They flap and sail low
over the dunes of the Long Island barrier beaches, cross
the water to the New Jersey shore, and continue south
to Cape May, where they sometimes congregate overnight in great numbers before crossing Delaware Bay
the next morning. They fly on and on in brisk head-
winds and crosswinds, moving steadily toward Florida
and other southern wintering areas. Monarchs also
move down the Pacific coast to winter in Southern California and Mexico.

Monarchs often soar aloft in thermals and travel
swiftly downwind when the wind blows the way they
are heading. They flap and sail along until they feel
lift; then they spin around and circle upward on motionless, outstretched wings. After rising hundreds of

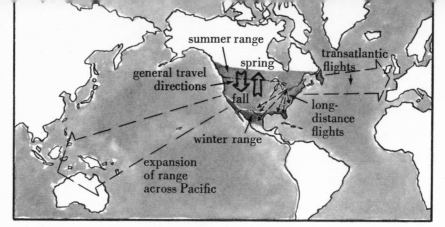

summer range

spring

general travel
directions

transatlantic
flights

fall

long-
distance
flights

winter range

expansion
of range
across Pacific

migrations of the monarch butterfly

*monarch butterflies
roosting during migration*

*monarch butterfly
on milkweed*

feet, they glide straight out in their direction of travel. As they gradually descend, they search for the next thermal to regain altitude. By repeating this maneuver many times, monarchs cover long distances with a minimum of wing flapping and conserve their energy.

A Canadian scientist, Doctor Frederick Urquhart, has developed a way to band butterflies by folding a numbered adhesive tab over the leading edge of the wing. With this technique he has gathered information on the amazing distances that individual monarch butterflies travel. The longest trip recorded to date is that of a monarch banded on September 18, 1957, at Highland Creek, Ontario, and recovered at San Luis Potosí, Mexico, on January 25, 1958. The straight line distance between the two points is 1870 miles, but the insect no doubt traveled in a more roundabout way and must have covered more than 2000 miles. The fastest long-distance trip was that of a monarch flying 1060 miles in 18 days, or an average of 59 miles per day. Short flights at faster rates of speed also have been noted. One monarch banded in Rockport, Texas, was recaptured two days later 260 miles away, an average of 130 miles per day. Strong tail winds were blowing.

The host plant of the monarch butterfly is the milkweed, which did not exist in Europe until recent years. However, the first sighting of a monarch in England was recorded long ago in 1876. Since then more than 200 have been observed in Europe. At one time scientists thought that these monarchs must have traveled on ships. They could not believe that the apparently fragile creatures were capable of flying across 3000 miles of ocean nonstop. However, in 1880, several eastbound monarchs were seen from a ship 400 miles out in the Atlantic Ocean from Scotland. Apparently they were making a transoceanic journey, and such evidence continues to accumulate.

It has been estimated that monarch butterflies can fly for up to 117 hours nonstop at 5.6 miles per hour in calm air. Thus, they can travel 650 miles nonstop under their own power. Aided by prevailing westerly winds that often blow for days at a time over the Atlantic Ocean at well over 20 miles per hour, monarchs would be able to make the trip easily. In the same way monarchs, starting in about 1850, were able to spread their breeding range westward from California to Java by island hopping 9000 miles across the Pacific Ocean.

Certainly they seem to be the greatest insect travelers of all.

Another great butterfly traveler is the painted lady. This species is found on every continent except South America, having spread far and wide by its lengthy migrations. Painted ladies often have been sighted more than 1000 miles out in the Atlantic Ocean, in the far North beyond the Arctic Circle, and over the mountains of Pakistan at 17,000 feet.

The painted ladies that arrive in Europe each spring come from winter breeding areas on the edge of the North African desert. The summer breeding range extends to Scotland and northern Germany. In some years, however, when very large populations occur, the butterfly may migrate as far north as northern Finland and Iceland. There, beyond the growing regions of thistle and other host plants, the insects cannot breed. These migrations may serve to lessen population pressure in the normal breeding range.

In North America, painted ladies winter in the semiarid regions of western Mexico. In spring, they fly northward, sometimes in tremendous numbers. One flock measured forty miles across and took three full days to pass the observation point. Successive generations of painted ladies travel into Canada, and even into Newfoundland, 3000 miles from their winter home.

A close relative of the painted lady, the American, or Hunter's, painted lady, is famous for one spectacular nonstop journey. In April, 1944, three males and three females of this species were captured on Tristan da Cunha Island in the South Atlantic. In the same week, several species of South American moths also were captured there. Scientists concluded, therefore, that the flight of the butterflies probably had originated in South America, whose nearest point was 2000 miles away.

Most butterflies lay their eggs on plants that are of little value to man. On the other hand, most moths lay their eggs on crops or trees. Accordingly, man classifies moths as destructive insects and studies their migrations more carefully than those of butterflies.

In China, the larvae of oriental armyworm moths are a serious threat to wheat and rice crops. Each spring in northeast China, adult moths suddenly appear over large regions. Evidently they migrate from distant southern provinces, where they are known to winter. To

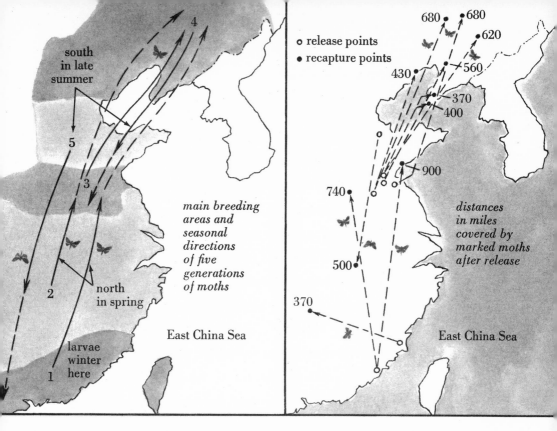

Within the figure:

south
in late
summer

5

3

2

north
in spring

larvae
winter
here

1

4

main breeding
areas and
seasonal
directions
of five
generations
of moths

East China Sea

o release points
• recapture points

680   •680

•620

430•   560

370
400

900

740•

500•

370

distances
in miles
covered by
marked moths
after release

East China Sea

migrations of the oriental armyworm moth in China

check this supposition, Chinese scientists marked great numbers of moths with colored dye and released them at various points farther south. A widespread trapping network recaptured a number of moths, as far as 900 miles to the north in spring and 500 miles to the south in autumn. Careful study showed that succeeding generations of oriental armyworm moths migrate north in spring and summer, then south in late summer and fall. There the larvae spend the winter.

Some moths have made amazingly long flights. Lesser armyworm moths are native to North Africa and rarely are seen in England. In 1962, however, 1200 of these moths were captured in England, and scientists tried to find out if they actually had traveled from North Africa. One large group of 100 moths had landed at Brockenhurst, in Hampshire, in the evening of May 6. By consulting weather charts for the preceding days, the scientists found that on May 2, in the interior of Morocco, where the moths breed, easterly winds blew toward the Atlantic Ocean and thermal lift was strong up to 5000 feet. On these winds the moths must have flown west, reaching the coast about noon on May 2. There they continued out over the Atlantic Ocean for another twenty-four hours before intercepting a southerly airstream. The moths then swung northeast and flew faster on increasingly strong southwest winds from a low pressure system off Portugal. By the evening of May 6, the moths reached England on winds of forty miles per hour. At that time rain and cold temperature of fifty-two degrees forced many of them down.

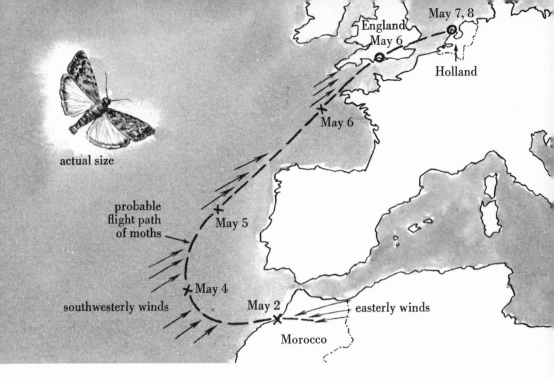

a flight of lesser armyworm moths from Africa to England

The accuracy of this flight track was confirmed when other lesser armyworm moths arrived in Holland on May 7 and 8. These insects had flown twelve hours more along the same path journeying nonstop from 1500 to 2000 miles.

Sometimes great numbers of moths are carried for long distances. At the end of June, 1958, millions of small and delicate diamondback moths invaded the British Isles and were seen from an ocean weather ship

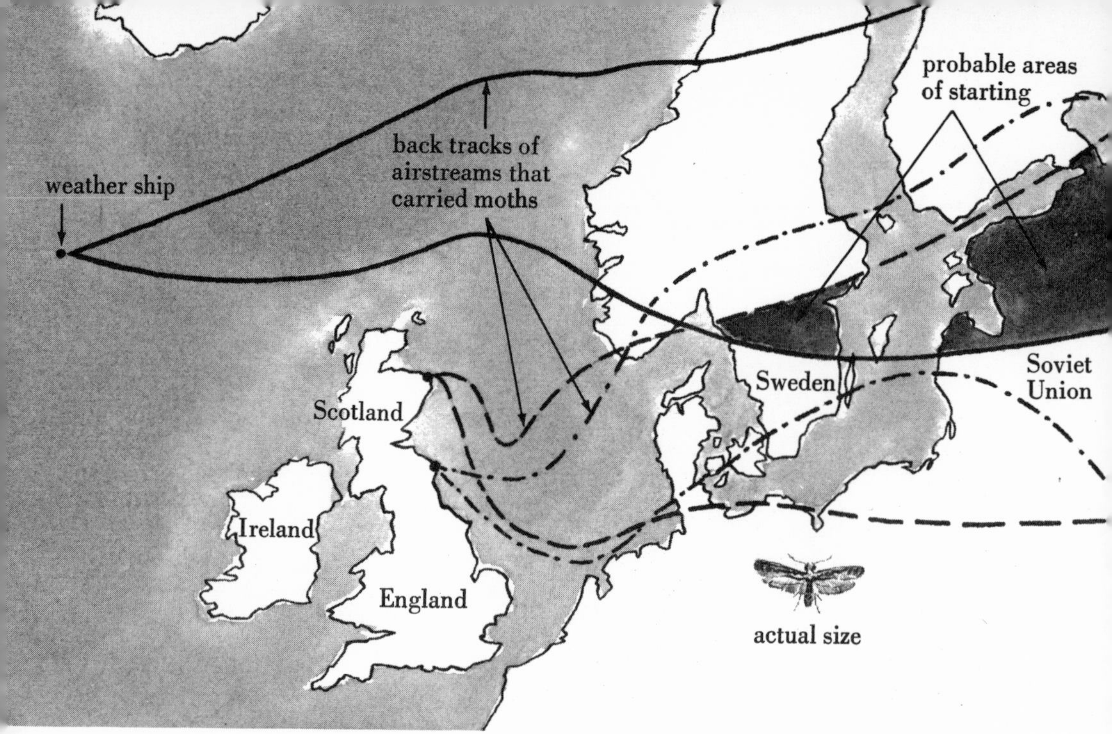
probable areas
of starting
back tracks of
airstreams that
carried moths
weather ship
Scotland
Sweden
Soviet
Union
Ireland
England
actual size

long westward migrations by millions of diamondback moths

500 miles west of Scotland and 300 miles north of Ireland. Airstreams carrying the moths came from 1500 to 2000 miles to the east in southern Sweden, the western Soviet Union, or even farther. These supposedly weak fliers had beat their wings, probably without a stop, for as long as four to five days.

One of the strangest examples of a long-distance insect flight involved a rush veneer moth captured in England in 1960. It was a very pale specimen, of a type that English scientists long had suspected came from North Africa, where these moths are much paler than those native to Europe. When Professor H. B. D. Kettlewell learned that the French were testing atomic bombs in North Africa in February, he envisioned the possibility that insects migrating from there could be marked by radioactive fallout. Accordingly, he made a strenuous effort to collect as many moths as possible in Europe during the period following the bomb tests. One pale rush veneer captured at Oxford, England, on March 10 had a small radioactive particle attached to its body. The particle's radioactive state showed that it came from a nuclear explosion in the Algerian Sahara Desert on February 13.

After checking air movements at that time, scientists decided that the particle had fallen to earth on February 17 or 18, where the moth probably picked it up from a plant. The moth then must have started traveling on easterly winds, reaching the northwest coast of Africa by February 26. On that day it could have entered an airstream moving out to sea west of Portugal and veering northeastward to England. By the time it landed this moth had traveled 1500 miles.

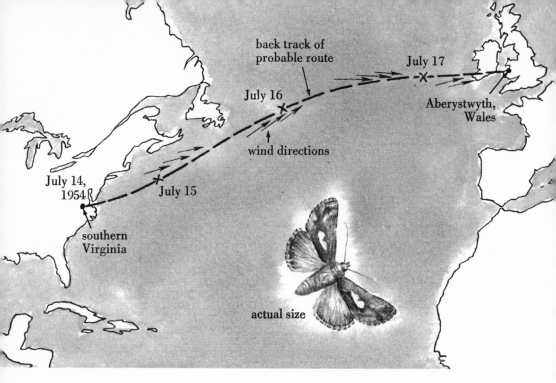

back track of
probable route

July 17

July 16

Aberystwyth,
Wales

wind directions

July 14,
1954

July 15

southern
Virginia

actual size

a transatlantic flight by the bilobed looper moth

Still another species of moth, one with an inch and
a half wingspan, has crossed the Atlantic Ocean. It is
the bilobed looper, a brownish moth with white wing
patches. Native to North America, it is seen only rarely
in Europe. On July 19, 1954, a single bilobed looper
was captured in Wales, at Aberystwyth. During the
two previous days, strong westerly winds had been blowing. After studying weather charts, scientists decided
that it had arrived on a strong, continous west-southwest

airstream from southern Virginia in the United States. The trip apparently had lasted three and a half days and had covered more than 3000 miles of the Atlantic Ocean.

Another bilobed looper was captured in Devon, England, on October 1, 1958. Again weather charts showed that a continuous flow of air had been blowing previously from North America. The fact that two native American birds, a northern water thrush and a Baltimore oriole, also were sighted in western England about October 1 was added evidence that the moth did cross the Atlantic Ocean.

Among the fastest and strongest insect fliers are the dragonflies, and sometimes they travel long distances. Little is known about their migrations, however, partly because their swift, darting flight and invisible, transparent wings make them hard to spot or to follow unless they are in large swarms. Some dragonflies seem to travel in calm periods preceding storms. Millions of four-spotted libellula dragonflies appear on the north German island of Helgoland before thunderstorms. Swarms of green darners also fly at such times in the United States. Other species have been sighted riding

green darner dragonflies traveling south in autumn

up on the strong lift of thunderstorm clouds, probably
in pursuit of insects carried aloft.

Dragonflies frequently migrate at low levels, where
they follow prominent features of the terrain. Large
flights of several species are seen in autumn funneling
through narrow mountain passes in the Swiss Alps, the
Pyrenees between France and Spain, and in Venezuela
as well as many other places. In the United States,
green darners follow the Atlantic shoreline south along

with birds and monarch butterflies. However, unlike monarchs, they lead short lives. The nymphs spend the winter in northern regions, so the adults do not migrate south in fall to insure survival of their species. Instead, their southward movement may be an escape flight toward warmer regions to prolong their brief lives.

Great flights of dragonflies, which take hours to pass a given point, have been reported from many parts of the world. In 1947, a series of dragonfly invasions descended upon the region around Cork, in southwest Ireland. On August 15, a strange hum was heard near the shore, growing louder and louder. Soon the sky was filled with millions of small, dark sympetrum dragonflies coming from the south over the sea. The swarms that darkened the sky were so thick that many people thought locusts had invaded. Other huge flights arrived on August 16 and 30, as well as on September 2 and 3. One swarm, a compact column about eight feet wide, streamed past Galley Head, Cork, for about half an hour, while another passed from noon until evening.

Weather charts for August 13 to 16 showed that the flights probably had started from northern Spain, where

dragonflies from Spain invading Ireland

that particular race of sympetrum breeds. Climbing several thousand feet in strong thunderstorm lift, they entered an airstream moving north to Ireland. Similarly the dragonflies that reached Ireland at the end of August probably climbed into fast, high-altitude winds over Spain on August 30, when strong thermals were rising up to 20,000 feet.

The longest known flight made by dragonflies occurred in 1969, when numbers of the North African species *Hemianax ephippiger* were found in Iceland. Weather charts showed that these dragonflies almost certainly had flown on a warm airstream from the southeast, starting in southern Italy or northern Libya in North Africa. In three days they traveled 2500 miles nonstop.

Many other long-range journeys have been made by various insects, such as locusts from North Africa flying nonstop to England. Again and again, small-winged creatures have shown their amazing ability to travel great distances on the wind.

III
Flight Power

At twilight, after a hot day in Morocco, a great flock of lesser armyworm moths rises across the sky and flies on into the night. Strong winds aloft steer them out over the coast, and when dawn comes the moths find themselves flying above an endless sweep of ocean with no place to land. Although they normally fly only

lesser armyworm moths

at night, the armyworm moths continue beating their small dark-gray wings all the next day. Night comes again, and they keep flying on, their flight muscles steadily draining the energy reserves from their small bodies.

When another day dawns, some of the moths stop flapping, descend, hit the choppy water, and flutter a moment before they drown. The other moths stay aloft and struggle on. Finally, after several nights and days, a small remnant of the original flock reaches land. The armyworm moths alight on plants. Their wings are frayed at the edges, and much of the gray brown color of their scales has rubbed off. The travelers are limp, quivering, and almost completely exhausted. Still, they have crossed almost 2000 miles of ocean nonstop and exceeded their normal travel time and distance many times over.

Winged insects travel by using the power of their flight muscles, burning the energy stored within their bodies for fuel. However, they are such small creatures that the amount of fuel they can carry is sharply limited. Where do they get the power and endurance to cross continents and span the seas?

Surprisingly, small size can sometimes be advantageous. For example, insects are comparatively stronger than man. A harvester ant can easily lift a pebble fifty times its own weight with its jaws. To match that feat a man would have to be capable of lifting four tons with his teeth. A grasshopper jumps thirty inches. To equal its performance, an Olympic athlete would need to broad jump two hundred feet instead of about twenty-seven feet.

Although insect muscle fiber has just about the same strength as human muscle, small size gives insects an advantage. The power of a muscle is determined by its flat, cross-sectional size, while the body weight to be moved by that muscle depends upon three-dimensional size, or volume. Thus, the larger the creature, the more weight it has to move in proportion to its muscle power. For this reason a small insect has greater relative strength than a man.

The structure of insects is very efficient. They are invertebrates, so their body shell provides their support. Their muscle fibers are short and thick, and they run directly from the walls of their body shells to the muscle tendons. Because of their small size, insects have short connecting nerves, so that impulses are transmitted rapidly through them. Accordingly, muscle efficiency is increased, allowing some insects to beat their wings at very high speeds. Short nerve lengths also explain why insects can react with such incredible quickness.

Flying insects are able to burn energy faster than any other creatures. As a result, they can maintain very intense levels of physical activity. The amount of energy a creature consumes while resting is called its basal metabolic rate. As muscular activity increases, the metabolic rate rises. The best human athlete can in-

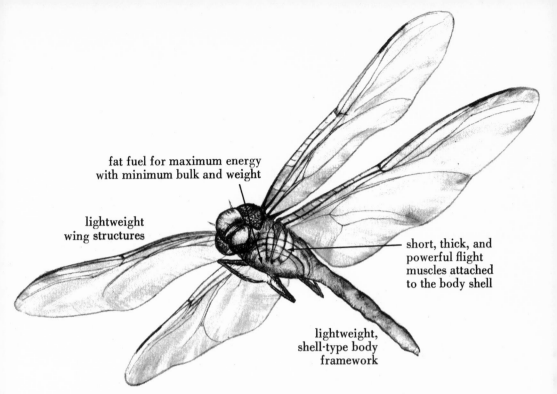

fat fuel for maximum energy
with minimum bulk and weight

lightweight
wing structures

short, thick, and
powerful flight
muscles attached
to the body shell

lightweight,
shell-type body
framework

some features that give flying insects high performance

crease his metabolic rate about twenty times, but only
for short periods. On the other hand, a flying insect
such as the locust can raise its metabolic rate more than
fifty times and can hold a rate of ten to twenty times
more than normal for a period of many hours.

How can insects carry enough fuel within their small
bodies to power flights that last hours and even days?
The answer lies in the kind of fuel that they use. It is

fat, which contains more energy for its bulk and weight than any other form of animal fuel. Most of an insect's fat is stored in the fat body, a layer beneath the outer shell of the thorax and abdomen sections. Smaller amounts are stored in other parts as a reserve.

Migrating insects burn energy at a much higher rate when they start out than during the rest of their trip. Experiments show that a locust's metabolic rate at the start of flight is three times greater and its airspeed considerably faster than later on. When insects take off and climb, they require plenty of wing lift and thrust, so their flight muscles have to work harder and burn more fuel to produce the needed power. In addition, various insects such as locusts, monarch butterflies, and small flies burn extra energy when they swarm in large masses before departing. After some time in the air, insects settle down to cruising speed. Then the rate of metabolism and fuel consumption drops to the most efficient level, allowing them to fly as far as possible on the smallest amount of fat.

In most cases, the amount of fat an insect carries at the start of migration determines how long it can travel. Locusts, monarch butterflies, dragonflies, and

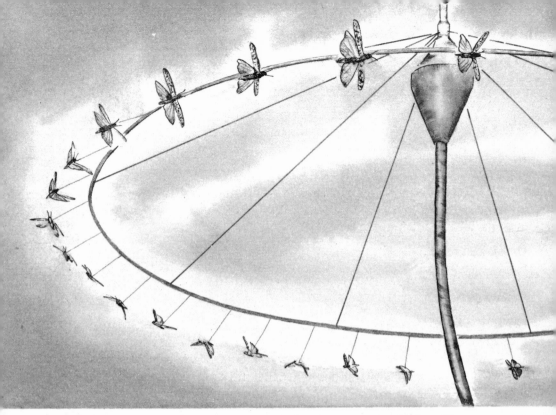

desert locusts in endurance test on a flight mill

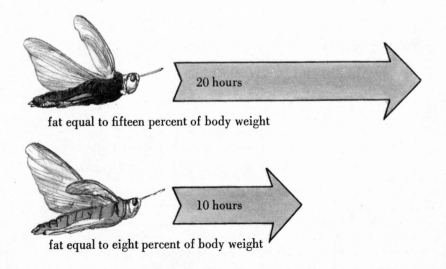

20 hours

fat equal to fifteen percent of body weight

10 hours

fat equal to eight percent of body weight

body fat and flight endurance in desert locusts

other insects feed before they depart to build up their fat supply. Other small insects—aphids and leafhoppers, for example—do not store up fat by feeding before migration, but are limited to the amount they have when they emerge as adults.

Not all insects in a flock start out with the same supply of fat, and those with the most travel the longest. To test this relationship between endurance and amount of fuel available, scientists have tethered African desert locusts to whirling flight mills so that their feet cannot touch any surface. Locusts with fat equal to eight percent of their body weight flew for ten hours, those with ten percent flew for thirteen hours, and those with a full load of fifteen percent flew for twenty hours. During their travels, locusts must sometimes cross wide stretches of arid land where little plant food exists. At such times, the ability to fly for several added hours can mean the difference between life and death.

While they travel most insects eat little or nothing. The fat supply they start out with decreases steadily with every beat of their wings. Short-range migrants like aphids and leafhoppers will not feed until the flight is over. On the other hand, long-range migrants that

Swarming desert locusts touch down to feed as they travel.

travel for a week or more must feed along the way to keep their fat supply from running out. For example, monarch butterflies heading south can be seen now and then stopping briefly on blossoms to sip some nectar. At night they feed in their roosting places.

Unlike most other migrants, locusts feed frequently during their travels. Often, as a swarm moves across country, locusts descend, touch down for a short time to eat, then resume their progress. Thus, the swarm stays in contact with the ground as individual locusts circulate up and down. Since these fliers are feeding continually, they actually increase their fat reserves during the first month of migration.

The millions of tiny flying machines in a large locust swarm burn enormous quantities of fuel. The combined weight of the locusts runs from 13,000 to 19,000 tons. On a daily flight, lasting five to eight hours, the swarm needs 500 to 800 tons of fat, which equals the amount of calories per day required by one and a half million human beings. As a result, these locust swarms cause tremendous devastation.

Before monarch butterflies spread their bright wings toward the south, they fill up with nectar and store plenty of fat on their small, black bodies. Young adult monarchs, in Ontario, Canada, were found to have twenty-five percent of their body weight as fat after emerging from their pupa. Then they put on additional fat very rapidly. By the time they were starting to migrate in autumn, they had increased their fat supply to one hundred and twenty-five percent of their original body weight.

As monarchs travel their fat reserves decrease stead-

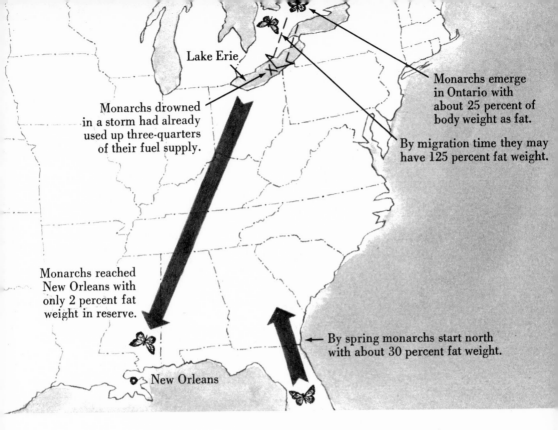

Lake Erie

Monarchs drowned
in a storm had already
used up three-quarters
of their fuel supply.

Monarchs emerge
in Ontario with
about 25 percent of
body weight as fat.

By migration time they may
have 125 percent fat weight.

Monarchs reached
New Orleans with
only 2 percent fat
weight in reserve.

By spring monarchs start north
with about 30 percent fat weight.

New Orleans

monarch fuel supply during migration

ily. If the trip is strenuous, fuel is depleted even more
rapidly. Scientists were able to examine one group of
monarchs that were caught by a sudden storm and
forced down into Lake Erie, where they drowned. Although they had traveled only a short distance from Ontario, the dead monarchs already had used up three
quarters of their fat supply battling the storm.

Even when conditions are good, monarch fat reserves run very low toward the end of the migration. A flock that arrived in New Orleans, Louisiana, after a long southward journey were reported to have fat supplies amounting to only two percent of their body weight. During their winter stay in the South, monarchs roost in a semidormant condition and burn very little energy. On warm days they become active and fly out to feed. By the time spring arrives, they have put on fat reserves equal to thirty percent of their body weight and are ready for the trip back to the North.

Many insects, including butterflies, aphids, and dragonflies, are lightly insulated and thus depend upon the sun's heat to remain active. Moths, however, have a coat of body scales that enclose a thin layer of insulating air. Since most moths fly at night when the air is cool, their structure is helpful for it enables them to maintain their body temperature at as much as sixty degrees above that of the outside air. Moths also rely upon muscular activity for body heat, as when they pump their wings rapidly to warm up before takeoff.

Chinese scientists found that oriental armyworm moths continued flapping for thirty-six hours at temperatures as low as sixty-two degrees. Since the metabolic rate decreases at low temperatures, these moths flew longer while burning less energy. Thus, instead of forcing them to stop flapping, moderately cold air probably serves to increase the efficiency of migrating moths. Since they can fly in a much wider range of air temperatures than other insects, the fact that moths have made most of the known long-range journeys is not surprising.

Insects beat their wings to transform stored body energy into the forces of upward lift and forward thrust that carry them through the air. The speed of wingbeat depends on the insect's size, weight, wing area, and muscle power. Large wings do not have to beat as fast as small wings to produce the same amount of lift.

Heavy-bodied, small-winged insects like bees and flies beat their wings at a high speed, their flight is quick and direct, and they burn fuel rapidly. Light-bodied, large-winged insects such as butterflies and moths flap their broad wings more slowly, fly at an easier pace, and do not burn fuel so fast. Nevertheless, they can put on surprisingly swift bursts of speed. Dragonflies, probably the fastest fliers of all, are in a class of their own. Their

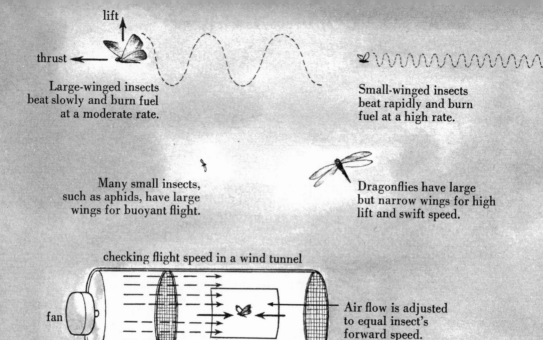

lift

thrust ←

Large-winged insects
beat slowly and burn fuel
at a moderate rate.

Small-winged insects
beat rapidly and burn
fuel at a high rate.

Many small insects,
such as aphids, have large
wings for buoyant flight.

Dragonflies have large
but narrow wings for high
lift and swift speed.

checking flight speed in a wind tunnel

fan

Air flow is adjusted
to equal insect's
forward speed.

insect fliers

long, narrow wings beat at moderate speeds, so dragonflies use relatively little fuel and can stay aloft for
hours. In addition, they feed on flying insects, which
enables them to refuel while in flight.

Insect flight speeds are very difficult to determine
in the field. Wind velocity and direction, temperature,
the insect's age, the purpose of the flight—migration,
food gathering, egg laying—are some of the factors that
affect the measurement. Very few field observations of

insect speed take all of them into account. But flying speeds can be measured more accurately in laboratory wind tunnels. There the scientist adjusts the airflow speed so that the wind blowing toward a tethered or free-flying insect is strong enough to keep it stationary as it flaps. Airflow speed then is equal to flight speed.

Insects fly at cruising speed during migration to conserve fuel energy. In autumn, monarch butterflies flap southward at a leisurely pace with shallow wingbeats. Migrating dragonflies and many other travelers often fly slower during migration than on their local flights. For this reason, scientists studying migrations are most interested in an insect's cruising speed. If they know that rate, the amount of fuel the insect burns each hour, and its weight of fat at takeoff, scientists can calculate its maximum range in calm air. Professor Brian Hocking has estimated this figure for a number of insects, some of which are listed in the chart on the following page.

Other insects have been test flown in laboratories to see how long they will continue flapping before exhaustion. Some of the longest flights have been made by army cutworm moths. Cruising at a speed of 2.3 to 5.8

	Wing Beats Per Second	Flight Speeds in Miles Per Hour	Calculated Maximum Range in Still Air (miles)
Fruit Fly (Drosophila)	250	2.4	30
Tabanid Fly (Tabanus affinis)	190	6.1-28	61
Mosquito (Aedes nearcticus)	600	2.5-5.5	30
Monarch Butterfly (Danaus plexippus)	8-10	5.7-12	650
Large Noctuid Moths	50-70	10-15	—
Dragonfly (Aeschna)	20-38	24-36	—
African Desert Locust (Schistocerca gregaria)	18-20	6.2-18	217

flight performance of various migrant insects

miles per hour, they have flown as long as 23 hours nonstop.

However, most species of insects do not begin to fly as long in laboratories as the same or similar species do on actual trips. Fully fueled African desert locusts have flown a maximum of 20 hours nonstop in tests. In contrast, the same species has traveled for 60 hours over the sea from Africa to the British Isles. Scientists cannot as yet account for these wide differences in performance. Further refinements in future tests no doubt will help to solve the present disparity between the flight endurance of insects in laboratories and those traveling out in the sun and the wind, over the forest and the sea.

Some insects do not fly with a constant, steady wing-beat. A number of butterflies, for example, flap several times and then glide for a short distance on outstretched wings. Repeated gliding conserves the insect's fuel energy and stretches its flight time and distance. Thus, the ability to glide is especially advantageous to migrating insects, although they lose altitude while doing so.

Another form of insect flight is that of soaring. In this case the insect maintains altitude or climbs higher by flying within rising thermal currents. Interestingly, the use of thermals is not limited to insects that glide. Aphids and leafhoppers rarely or never glide, but they are able to soar by flapping their wings just enough to keep their equilibrium while they are carried upward. On days of powerful thermal activity, even nonflying insects such as small wingless ants and larvae are lifted

steady gliding

Insects gain or maintain altitude on rising air.

gliding between wing beats

soaring

insects gliding and soaring

Butterflies and moths have large wings and can soar in moderate thermal lift.

Dragonflies can soar in strong thermal lift.

Small bouyant fliers like aphids flap their wings while rising.

Locust swarm rises in a thermal.

rising bubble of heated air

thermal shell forming

from the ground and carried high. In general, however, lightweight, large-winged insects like butterflies and small, buoyant insects such as aphids ride thermals most easily. The lighter the load an insect carries, the less lift it needs to soar.

On clear, dry days, monarchs and other butterflies circle upward on motionless wings within rising thermal bubbles in the same way that soaring hawks and gulls do. Locusts billow aloft in towering swarms that outline the thermals carrying them. Dragonflies stop flapping for minutes at a time while they circle and soar on high. Swarms of winged ants, termites, aphids, leafhoppers, and many other insects are boosted up and away as they start their migrations.

Once insects have climbed aloft, they are able to ride the faster winds that blow at higher levels. If their trip lasts a day or less, local winds usually carry insects in one steady direction. The longer insects remain in flight, however, the greater effect winds have on the speed, distance, and direction of their journey. During a trip of several days or weeks, the travelers may enter complex airstreams caused by large-scale weather systems moving across continents and oceans. Sometimes in-

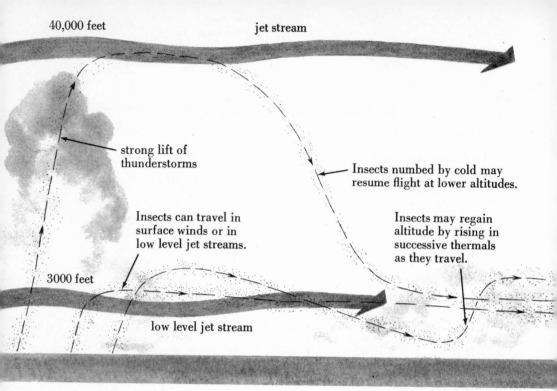

40,000 feet   jet stream

strong lift of
thunderstorms

Insects numbed by cold may
resume flight at lower altitudes.

Insects can travel in
surface winds or in
low level jet streams.

Insects may regain
altitude by rising in
successive thermals
as they travel.

3000 feet

low level jet stream

ways that migrating insects can use the wind

sects follow the same airstream for thousands of miles,
as when monarch butterflies cross the Atlantic Ocean.
At other times, insects may go from one airstream to
another like passengers at a transfer point.

Occasionally insects rising in the powerful lift of
thunderstorm winds may be able to reach extremely
high altitudes of 30,000 to 40,000 feet. There jet
streams blow at 100 miles per hour or more over great

distances. Insects cannot remain active in the air temperatures at these altitudes for any lengh of time, but a high-altitude jet stream could give them a terrific starting boost. After being numbed by cold, they might resume flying after falling into the warmer air of low-level jet streams found at 1000 to 3000 feet or into even lower airstreams. Whatever the pattern, wind is essential to the long-distance flights of all insect travelers.

Insects gain their power to travel from muscles and the fat supply that fuels them. Their wings beat to carry them over the ground at low levels or to climb high. Thermal lift helps them to gain and regain altitude, while winds multiply their speed and the distance of the journeys.

IV
Finding
Their
Way

A ship moves east through the long, gentle swells of the Mediterranean Sea on a clear morning in July. Every so often, from the south, a butterfly appears, flying just above the surface. It does not turn to avoid the ship, but flutters straight up the side, crosses the deck, and continues on the exact same course as before.

painted lady butterfly following a straight course

The butterfly is a painted lady, migrating north to Europe from North Africa. Although in this instance each painted lady is flying alone, all the butterflies are moving in the identical northward direction.

Instances such as this one have led scientists to wonder how insects can follow a steady course when they travel. To find its way, a creature must receive reliable cues from its surroundings by way of its senses. Undoubtedly vision, as one might suspect from the size of their huge, bulging eyes, is the sense that insects use above all others to move from place to place.

Insects have compound eyes made up of many individual lens facets that transmit separate images to their brains. There they are formed into a composite picture. This process is quite different from the way the single lens of a man's eye works. The human eye forms a sharp, unified image, while the insect eye creates a more blurred, mosaic image. Although insects do not receive photographically sharp and detailed pictures of the outside world, they can recognize objects by their patterns and shapes.

The simplest visual method of finding and following a course is to look for known landmarks. This is how a student finds his way to school or a shopper locates a certain store. To orient himself by means of landmarks, the traveler must remember familiar features of the terrain. Some species of ants remember particular stones, twigs, or whatever and use them as a guide to and from their nesting hole. Honeybees often follow landmarks when flying back and forth to their hive. Dragonflies find the same perching twig again and again by using their memory of objects in the immediate vicinity.

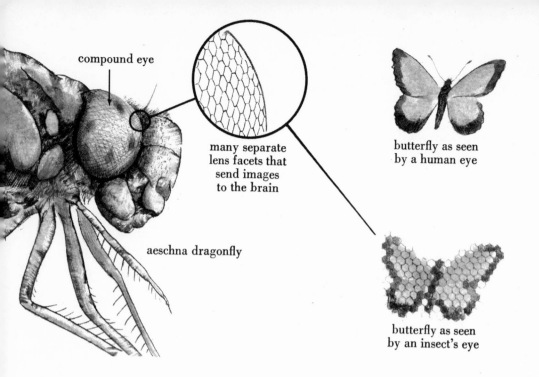

compound eye

many separate
lens facets that
send images
to the brain

aeschna dragonfly

butterfly as seen
by a human eye

butterfly as seen
by an insect's eye

the insect's compound eye

However, landmark orientation can be of use to insects only as they move within a limited breeding habitat. When the great majority of insects migrate, they see completely unfamiliar places for the first time, so they can have no memory of landmarks along the way. The only possible exception would be those long-lived insects such as monarch butterflies and ladybird beetles that migrate more than once. They might recognize features of the terrain seen on an earlier trip. Still, sect can locate the sun's position accurately. In fact, insects rely upon the sun's position to set and follow a course.

The use of the sun compass in the animal world was first discovered among insects years ago. Later it also was found to be an important guide to the movements of birds, mammals, fish, and other creatures. Scientific knowledge of the sun compass began with a study of desert ants.

In 1911, the Italian zoologist Felix Santschi noticed that desert ants in North Africa followed a straight course across barren stretches of sand on feeding trips even where there were no landmarks in sight. Santschi suspected that the ants might be using the sun to keep their bearings. He shaded the sun from the direct view of the ants and used a mirror to reflect its image from a different angle. As soon as the sun's apparent position was shifted, the ants turned and changed their course. The new course differed from the original one by exactly the angle between the sun's real position and the artificial position. By moving the sun's image with the mirror, Santschi could steer the ants in any direction, even directly away from the nesting hole that they were seeking. He had demonstrated clearly that the ants were using the sun to guide their travels.

The use of the sun compass is a complex process. As an insect travels, the sun's position changes. During the day the sun arcs across the sky from east to west. If an insect is heading north in the morning, the sun will be ninety degrees to its right. If it continues to keep the sun ninety degrees to its right, its own heading will swing first to the east, then to the south as the afternoon sun moves to the west. Thus, by afternoon the insect will be heading in exactly the opposite direction of its original northward course. To follow a steady path, the insect must allow for the continual change of the sun's position during the day. Thus, an inner sense of time is essential to sun-compass orientation.

An insect may start out by setting its course on the horizon point directly below the sun. To hold its direction, the insect keeps the sun's image centered within the frame of a single eye facet. But the sun keeps moving. Accordingly, the insect shifts its view of the sun every so often to the proper adjoining facet. A honeybee, for example, shifts the sun's image about once every ten minutes to stay on course. Its inner clock,

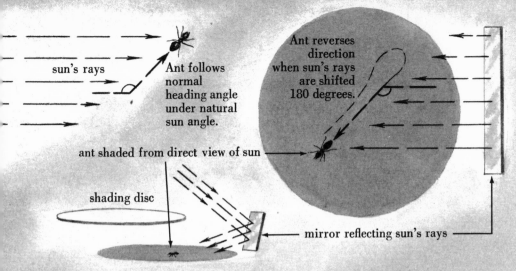

sun's rays

Ant follows normal heading angle under natural sun angle.

Ant reverses direction when sun's rays are shifted 180 degrees.

ant shaded from direct view of sun

shading disc

mirror reflecting sun's rays

the sun compass of African desert ants

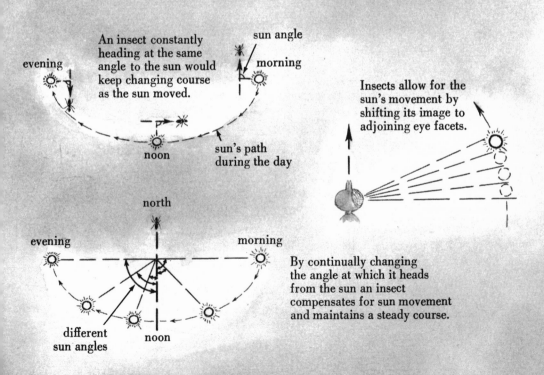

An insect constantly heading at the same angle to the sun would keep changing course as the sun moved.

sun angle

evening

morning

noon

sun's path during the day

Insects allow for the sun's movement by shifting its image to adjoining eye facets.

north

evening

morning

different sun angles

noon

By continually changing the angle at which it heads from the sun an insect compensates for sun movement and maintains a steady course.

how insects use the sun compass

therefore, must measure intervals of time accurately.

After Santschi discovered that ants used the sun to find their way, he observed that they still could stay on course when their direct view of the sun was blocked. Puzzled, Santschi thought the ants might be able to see the stars in the daytime sky and were taking bearings from them. Some years later Karl von Frisch of Austria observed that honeybees navigated with no trouble on partly cloudy days when the sun was obscured and only patches of blue sky were visible. Von Frisch did not believe that ants or bees could see the stars during the day. Instead, he suspected that certain characteristics of the light from the blue sky itself might serve as a guide.

Light ordinarily vibrates in all directions at right angles to the ray that produces it. However, light passing through the earth's atmosphere is diffused and reflected, so that it vibrates in one plane and is said to be polarized. Since the sun's rays pass through the atmosphere at different angles, polarized light from each part of the blue sky vibrates in a different plane. As the sun's position changes during the day, the overall sky pattern of polarized light also changes.

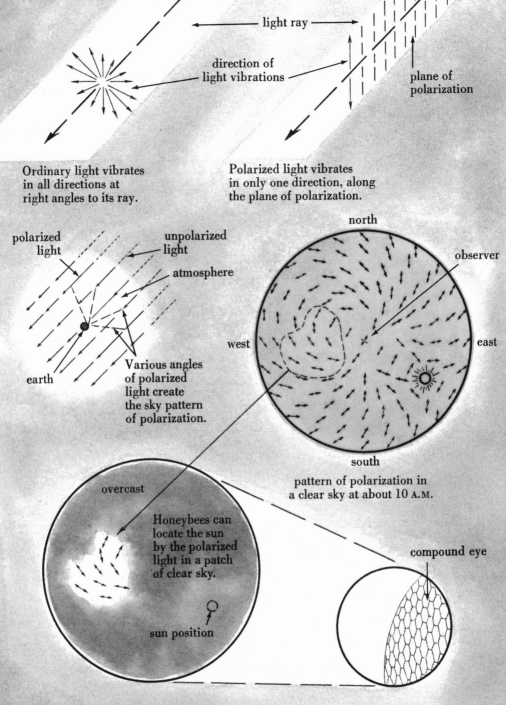

light ray

direction of
light vibrations

plane of
polarization

Ordinary light vibrates
in all directions at
right angles to its ray.

Polarized light vibrates
in only one direction, along
the plane of polarization.

polarized
light

unpolarized
light

atmosphere

earth

Various angles
of polarized
light create
the sky pattern
of polarization.

north

observer

west

east

south

pattern of polarization in
a clear sky at about 10 A.M.

overcast

Honeybees can
locate the sun
by the polarized
light in a patch
of clear sky.

sun position

compound eye

Insects use polarized light to find their way.

Von Frisch speculated that perhaps insects could guide themselves by the sky's total polarized light pattern when the sun was hidden. A patch of blue sky would be all that they needed. He tested honeybees, using a special Polaroid filter to polarize the daylight entering the hive through a narrow stovepipe. When a honeybee returns from foraging, it runs in certain patterns on the inner wall of the hive to show other bees the flight direction to the food. At first von Frisch set the filter so that the plane of polarization was the same as that of natural daylight. The bees indicated a certain direction. Then he turned the filter and shifted the plane of polarization. Immediately the bees changed their direction by exactly the same angle.

With this experiment von Frisch explained the mysterious ability of the ants that had puzzled Santschi. Ants, wasps, bumblebees, as well as some flies and beetles, have been shown to react to the polarized light of the blue sky. Because sky polarization depends upon the sun's position, scientists think insects use it in connection with the sun compass rather than as a substitute. If the sun is visible, insects probably use it directly.

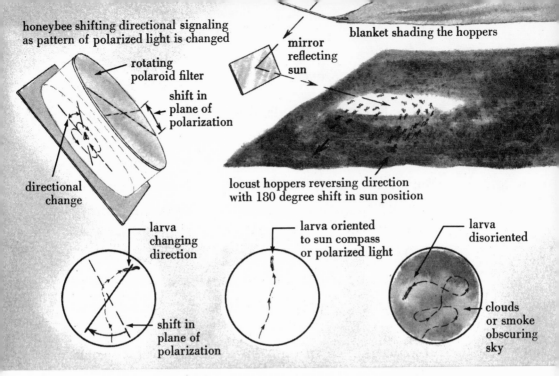

honeybee shifting directional signaling as pattern of polarized light is changed

rotating polaroid filter

shift in plane of polarization

directional change

mirror reflecting sun

blanket shading the hoppers

locust hoppers reversing direction with 180 degree shift in sun position

larva changing direction

shift in plane of polarization

larva oriented to sun compass or polarized light

larva disoriented

clouds or smoke obscuring sky

Insects respond to shifts of polarized light and sun position.

Desert ants and honeybees were the first insects known to navigate with the sun and polarized light. But African desert ants and European honeybees are not migrant insects. They have regular nesting places and leave them only on short feeding trips. Because their location is fixed, such insects are easier to observe than freely migrating insects whose destination is usually unknown. There is some evidence, however, that a number of migrating insects also use the sun compass.

J. S. Kennedy of England found that both immature desert locusts, or hoppers, as well as the winged adults show a clear reaction to the sun when they are on the ground. For example, when the sun was shining from the east, he shaded hoppers marching north with a blanket. Then he reflected the sun's image from the west by mirror. Responding to this 180-degree shift in sun direction, all the hoppers turned 180 degrees and marched south. By continually shifting the apparent position of the sun, Professor Kennedy made the hoppers change their marching direction again and again.

In another experiment, the larvae of certain flies, moths, and beetles crawling beneath a Polaroid filter changed their directions accordingly when the pattern of polarization was shifted. In addition, clouds or smoke hiding the image of the sun and the clear blue sky overhead caused these larvae to become disoriented. Some circled around, others kept changing direction rapidly, while still others stopped crawling completely until the sky was clear again.

Of all migrants, butterflies give the clearest indication of using the sun for navigation. Certainly they show a strong dependence upon a compass course. In

East Africa, a steady procession of white butterflies that lasted for several days flew up one side of a cottage and down the other, instead of swerving off course to avoid the obstacle. Scientists believe that these and other butterflies use the sun compass in their travels, even though conclusive proof still is lacking.

Butterflies inherit the directions in which they migrate. In Europe, large flocks of the cabbage-white butterfly follow a southeast course in summer. One scientist in Germany raised cabbage whites in the laboratory, where they had no view of their natural surroundings. When they were ready to depart, he released them in a field and checked their flight headings as they started out. The great majority of the whites immediately headed southeast, the same direction in which the flocks travel. Since they had had no contact with the outdoors before their release, their flight directions must have been inborn, inherited from their parents. The same is probably true of many other young migrants.

How do insects find their way after dark, when there is no sun to steer by? Night-flying moths use the moon over short distances, holding a steady course by keeping a constant angle between it and their flight path.

Since the moon does not move too rapidly across the sky, it is a satisfactory guide point for shorter flights. But it is not suitable for longer flights as it lacks the sun's regularity of motion. The moon rises at a markedly different time each night and follows a different path across the sky. It is not even a constant feature of the night sky, since it is invisible during its new phase. Thus, except for short periods of time, the moon is difficult to use for navigation.

Perhaps insects can steer by the stars. Doctor Carl Cleve of Berlin found that moths should be able to see almost as many stars as man. Thus, brighter than average stars of the major constellations should be easily visible to moths. Since insect eyes are sensitive to both patterns and location of points within their field of view the existence of an insect star compass may be a possibility. Or perhaps night migrants do not take compass directions from any visual guide points, but simply follow the wind.

Insects are known for their keen sense of smell. Male moths and butterflies can perceive infinitesimally small concentrations of female scent attractants wafted on the breeze during the mating period. Butterflies,

Do insects steer by the stars?

moths, hover flies, mosquitoes, and many other insects fly upwind and follow airborne scent trails in search of food.

Probably there are times when scent is helpful to migrating insects. Night-traveling moths and butterflies may use their sense of smell to stay together in flocks in the dark. During the last part of migration, many butterflies, moths, and other insects fly upwind toward breeding places that they find by scent. Butterflies that

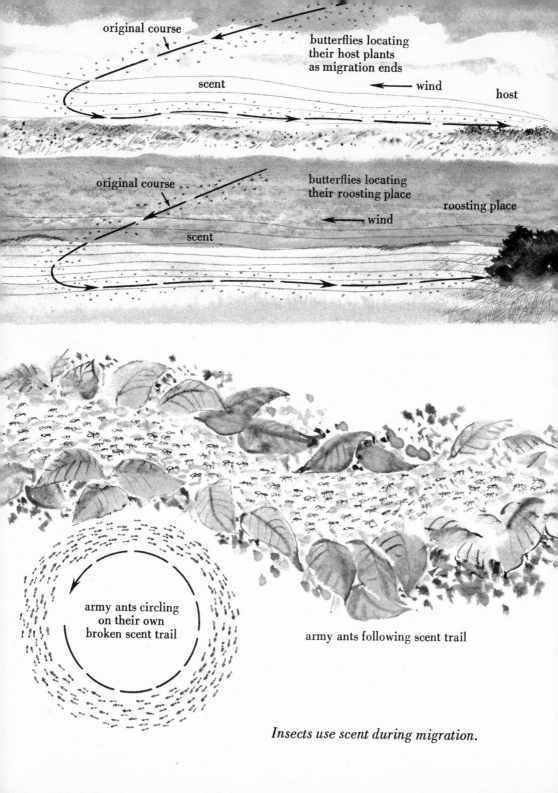

original course

butterflies locating
their host plants
as migration ends

scent

wind

host

original course

butterflies locating
their roosting place

roosting place

scent

wind

army ants circling
on their own
broken scent trail

army ants following scent trail

Insects use scent during migration.

travel the same general route year after year may locate traditional roosting places by the trace of scent that lingers on.

For example, monarch butterflies often roost overnight in evergreen groves as they travel down the shoreline of the eastern United States. Edwin Way Teale once observed southbound monarchs crossing Long Island, New York, when an east wind was blowing. Two hundred yards to the east there was a small grove of trees. Suddenly all the monarchs turned and headed for the grove. Teale believed that the scent remaining from monarchs roosting there in previous years was carried downwind to the butterflies.

Scent plays a vital part in the migrations of army ants of South America and driver ants of Africa. Since these ants have very poor vision or are totally blind, they coordinate their travels by passing scent signals along their line of march. When food is discovered or a new line of attack begins, scouts run back to inform the rest of the army by means of chemical messages. The ants signal by touching one another or by depositing tiny amounts of the scent on trails as they crawl. Their antennae have cells to detect the scent signals.

Normally the rough jungle terrain keeps the army ants from circling all the way around and linking up again with their own scent trail. Should such an accident happen, their absolute dependence on scent means their doom. On a sidewalk in Panama, where rain had washed away the scent trail, an ant column became separated from the main army. The column accidentally made a circle on the sidewalk, and the ants marched around and around, following their own scent trail, until they all died from exhaustion.

Migrating insects are very sensitive to wind speed and direction, which they detect by continually watching the ground images passing just below them. If a head wind should blow a butterfly backward over the ground, it will land. The butterfly's eyes cannot tolerate ground images moving in the wrong direction, and its brain signals for flying to cease. Similarly the butterfly cannot simply turn around and fly downwind at low levels, since its eyes also will not tolerate ground images flowing past at too high a speed.

The reason why insects can travel so fast during migration has been given by Professor Kennedy, who tested the sun compass of desert locusts. After studying

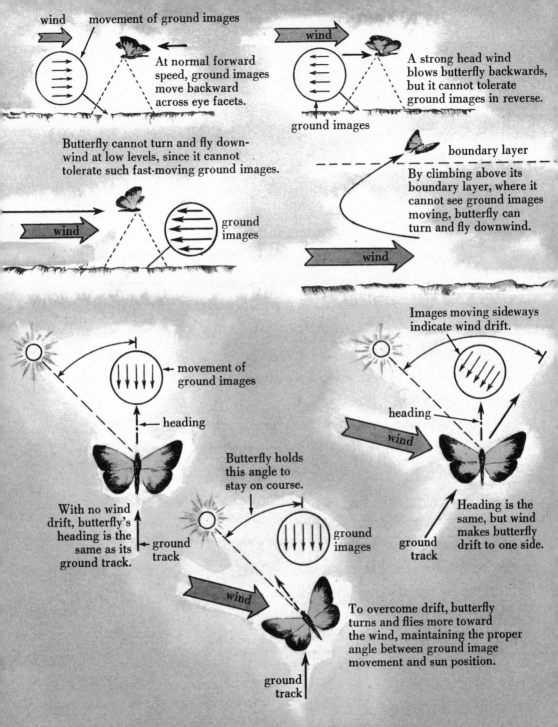

wind   movement of ground images

At normal forward speed, ground images move backward across eye facets.

A strong head wind blows butterfly backwards, but it cannot tolerate ground images in reverse.

ground images

Butterfly cannot turn and fly downwind at low levels, since it cannot tolerate such fast-moving ground images.

wind

ground images

boundary layer

By climbing above its boundary layer, where it cannot see ground images moving, butterfly can turn and fly downwind.

wind

Images moving sideways indicate wind drift.

movement of ground images

heading

heading

wind

Butterfly holds this angle to stay on course.

With no wind drift, butterfly's heading is the same as its ground track.

ground track

ground images

Heading is the same, but wind makes butterfly drift to one side.

ground track

wind

ground track

To overcome drift, butterfly turns and flies more toward the wind, maintaining the proper angle between ground image movement and sun position.

ground track

how wind affects insect orientation

the flight behavior of mosquitoes in wind tunnels, he concluded that in order to fly swiftly downwind, insects climb above the height where their eyes respond to ground patterns passing below. He called the distance from the ground to that critical height the insect's boundary layer. The boundary layer may be only a few inches for the smallest insects. For large fliers, with sharp vision, it may extend up to twenty-five feet or higher. When they depart on migration, many insects climb steeply to penetrate the top of their boundary layer. Higher up, unable to see the inhibiting ground images below, they are able to travel fast and far with the wind.

White butterflies in Argentina migrate at a low or high altitude depending upon the direction of the wind. When head winds blow, the whites fly close to the ground and avoid being pushed backward or drifted off course. When tail winds blow, the whites climb upward in large flocks, to 5000 feet or more, and travel swiftly downwind. They probably check the wind direction first by sun compass, then fly accordingly.

Low-flying insects also detect wind drift by checking the ground images. If the ground moves straight backwards, there is no drift. If it moves past at an angle to the left or right, there is a drifting effect. Larger insects migrating at low levels often compensate for crosswind drift by flying with their bodies pointed toward the wind. In Germany, cabbage-white butterflies held a steady southward course during several days of easterly winds by pointing their bodies southeast. Green darner dragonflies and monarch butterflies moving west along the south shore of Long Island, New York, point toward a northwest wind to avoid being drifted out to sea. C. B. Williams of England observed a flight of locusts in North Africa flying northeast in a gusty southeast wind. When the wind speed was low, the locusts pointed northeast, directly along their flight track. However, when a gust came from the right side, the locusts immediately swung their bodies toward the wind to maintain the same track.

African desert locusts rely upon prevailing wind directions to guide their migrations. They travel at times within their boundary layer and maintain course despite wind shifts by using the sun compass. Most of the time, however, desert locusts climb above their boundary layer, sometimes up to thousands of feet. There they mill around at random, and their only orientation consists of turning inward when they reach the outer edges of the swarm. The swarm as a whole is carried by prevailing winds away from the semiarid regions in which locusts travel to areas where greater amounts of rainfall occur. When locusts reach these regions, they lay eggs, which now have enough moisture to develop and hatch. Thus, locusts have insured their survival by using wind orientation during migration.

Teeming millions of insects descend like living rain on every mile of land and sea. Many of these travelers pollinate plants and trees, and without their help the world would be a paler, more barren place. Other travelers are destructive and come like winged armies on the wind to devour and destroy food crops and flowers, fruit, timber, and shade trees.

To combat the destruction, men spray powerful pesticides on plants and trees. But these substances also kill insect-eating birds as well as pest-eating insects such as dragonflies, ladybird beetles, and wasps. All are wiped out indiscriminately. Already man has changed the balance of nature with pesticides by reducing the numbers

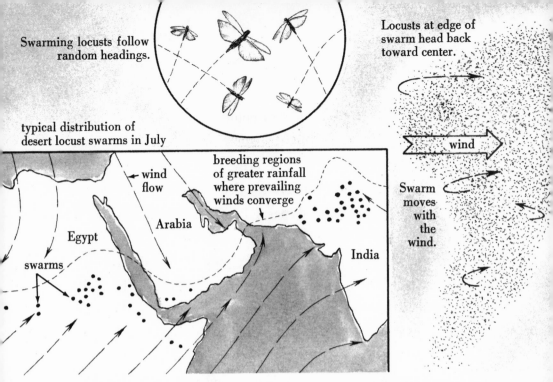

Swarming locusts follow random headings.

Locusts at edge of swarm head back toward center.

typical distribution of desert locust swarms in July

wind flow

breeding regions of greater rainfall where prevailing winds converge

Arabia

Egypt

India

swarms

wind

Swarm moves with the wind.

Desert locust swarms use prevailing winds for orientation.

of natural predators that once helped to check the insect pests. The deadly poisons seep into every nook and cranny of the environment and build up slowly in the living tissue of human beings, causing long-term damage that we just are beginning to identify.

The study of insect migration may provide man with a better way to combat pests that feed on crops and foliage. Helpful insects can be introduced into new regions. For example, Australian ladybird beetles were imported to California to combat scale insects. There they established themselves permanently, and now they migrate and attack their prey according to their own schedule. Insect predators also can be freed in the breeding habitats of pests in order to destroy them. Ladybird beetles and wasps are bred on insect farms and released at a time when they can feed on young aphids before the aphids mature and migrate. By using the right predators in the right places at the right times, man eventually may be able to rely mainly upon biological rather than chemical control of pests.

Biological control is being used now, but only on a small scale in scattered places. To be effective, a program of biological control must be worldwide. The nations involved could organize a network like that used for weather information, making full use of the latest technology. Recently great swarms of locusts have been tracked in India for several days across many miles with long-range radar. Such studies of pest movements would be of great help in wiping them out at their sources.

Meanwhile, insects surround us, familiar yet very remote creatures whose private world holds many wonders for the human observer. Perhaps you may want to catch them with a net, identify them, and examine their intricate, delicate structure or their multicolored wing scales with a magnifying glass. Then open the net and let them go. As they fly off, try to imagine where they come from and where they might be heading. They may be local residents, following their everyday routine. Or they may be travelers, whose small but powerful wings can drive them on and on or lift them sunward into the wind and far away.

Bibliography

(P) *means paperback*

von Frisch, Karl. *The Dancing Bees.* New York: Harvest Books, Harcourt Brace Jovanovich, Inc., 1953. (P)
  This classic study of the honeybee should be read by anyone interested in the senses, behavior, and navigation of insects.

Johnson, C. G. *Migration and Dispersal of Insects by Flight.* London: Methuen & Co. Ltd., 1969.

> The definitive work in this field. A carefully organized, detailed summary of all aspects of aerial migration, with an excellent bibliography. For the advanced student.

Johnson, C. G. "The Aerial Migration of Insects." *Scientific American,* December, 1963, pp. 132-138.

> A concise summary of the more recent theories of insect migration.

Mitchell, Robert T., and Zim, Herbert S. *Butterflies and Moths.* New York: Golden Books, 1964. (P)

> An introductory field guide that includes breeding range maps for many species.

Wigglesworth, V. B. *The Life of Insects.* New York: Mentor Books, The New American Library, Inc., 1968. (P)

> A clear, comprehensible survey of almost every aspect of insect life; particularly good on their structure and senses.

Williams, C. B. *Insect Migration.* London: Wm. Collins Sons & Co. Ltd., 1958.

> A compilation of many observations, especially of

butterflies and moths, by the outstanding pioneer in this field. Some of the ideas on orientation now out-of-date, but still well worth reading.

Zim, Herbert S. and Cottam, Clarence. *Insects.* New York: Golden Press, 1956. (P)

A beginner's guide to the most common insects.

Index

indicates illustrations

123

Born in New York City, John Kaufmann was educated at Brooklyn Technical High School, and the Pennsylvania Academy of Fine Arts. Later he studied and traveled extensively for a year in Europe. He now lives in Fresh Meadows, New York, with his wife and two sons. An established illustrator with a strong interest in nature writing for children, Mr. Kaufmann has a number of books to his credit.